CLASSICS *for* YOUNG READERS

Volume 3A

TABLE OF CONTENTS

LESSONS LEARNED

ANIMAL TALES

ANIMALS AND THEIR PEOPLE

TALES OF THE BROTHERS GRIMM

GREEK AND ROMAN MYTHS

POETRY

THE WORLD IS SO FULL

ANIMAL FRIENDS

NATURE'S WAY

LESSONS LEARNED

THE WIND AND THE SUN

One day, the Wind and the Sun exchanged words about which was the stronger.

"I am the stronger," puffed the Wind. "See how I can send the black clouds flying through the sky."

"No doubt you are strong," was the Sun's gentle reply. "But how can you prove that you are stronger than I?"

"I can soon prove that," said the Wind. "You see that man walking along the road? Let us agree that he is the stronger who can make the man take off his coat."

"Agreed!" said the Sun. "You may try first."

So the Wind blew a fierce blast. It blew harder and harder. But the man only turned his back to the Wind and wrapped his coat more closely around him.

In vain, the noisy Wind tried to blow the man's coat off. Then the Wind said to the Sun, "It is your turn to try now."

So the Sun sent some gentle rays down upon the man. Soon he became so warm that he was glad to unbutton his coat.

By and by he became so warm that he pulled off his coat and hung it on his arm.

Thus the gentle Sun proved that he was stronger than the noisy Wind. Gentle ways often prevail when rough ones fail.

THE BUNDLE OF STICKS

There once was a man whose family argued constantly. He had tried in many ways to teach them not to quarrel but had failed.

One day he called his sons together. He told them to lay a bundle of sticks before him. He tied a strong cord firmly around the bundle of sticks. He told his sons, one after the other, to take up the bundle and break it. They all tried, but they could not break the bundle.

Then the father untied the cord and gave his sons the sticks to break, one by one. They did this with the greatest ease.

Then the father said, "You are like the sticks, my sons. As long as you stand by each other, you are strong. You can do great things, meet any challenge, and stand up to any enemy. When you quarrel and separate, you are easily beaten. In unity there is strength."

– Aesop

WHY THE LARKS FLEW AWAY

A family of four young larks once lived with their mother in a nest in a wheat field. At first the nest was very safe, for it stood on the soft ground and was hidden by the wheat.

When the wheat began to ripen, the mother lark watched carefully for any sign of the coming of the reapers. She feared that the sharp knives would cut the nest and injure the young larks.

One morning she had to leave the nest to find some breakfast for her little ones.

"Be good children and stay in the nest," she said. "If the farmer and his son pass through the field, listen very carefully to what they say."

"Yes, Mother," cried the four baby larks.

The mother lark flew away. A few minutes later, the little larks heard the farmer and his son passing along the narrow path near the nest.

"This wheat is ripe enough to cut," said the farmer. "John, go down the road to Neighbor Smith's farmhouse and ask him to come tomorrow to help us reap the grain."

When the mother lark came home, she brought some fat worms for breakfast. She found her babies chirping excitedly.

"Mother, Mother!" they cried. "The men are coming to cut the wheat. We must move away tonight!"

"What did the farmer say?" asked the mother lark.

"The farmer told his son to go over to Neighbor Smith's house and ask him to help cut the grain."

"My dear children," laughed the mother lark, "as yet we have nothing to fear."

When the baby larks had eaten their breakfast, the mother lark showed them how to exercise their wings.

The next morning, before leaving the mother lark said once more, "Stay in the nest, and if the farmer passes through the field, listen to what he says."

"Yes, Mother," cried the little larks.

Away flew the mother, and again the farmer and his son passed through the fields.

"Did you ask Neighbor Smith to help us cut the grain?" inquired the farmer.

"Yes, Father," replied the son, "and I expected him here already."

"The wheat is ripe and it should be cut without delay," replied the farmer. "Mount your horse and ride to your cousins' house. Ask them if they will help us."

This frightened the baby larks so much that when they saw their mother coming, they began to chirp more loudly than ever.

"What is the trouble?" called the mother as she hastened toward the nest.

"We must surely go away today!" cried the young larks. "The farmer's son has gone to bring his cousins to cut the wheat. We shall be killed if we stay here."

Again the mother laughed. "If the farmer waits for his cousins to help him, the wheat will not be cut today."

The third morning, the mother left the nest to search for food. At noon the farmer and his son came into the field.

"See how late it is," said the farmer, "and still not a man has come to help us. I see we must do the work ourselves. Let us go home and get everything ready. Tomorrow, before the sun is up, we shall begin to reap."

Soon after the farmer had gone, the mother lark came flying over the wheat field. The little larks told her all that they had heard.

"Now, indeed, it is time for us to be off," she said. "Shake your wings and get ready to fly. When a man makes up his mind to do his own work, it is sure to be done at once."

ANIMAL TALES

Tug-of-War

Turtle liked to boast and brag. For such a small animal, he had a very big opinion of himself. He even claimed to be as powerful as the biggest animals, Elephant and Hippopotamus.

One day he said, "When Elephant and Hippopotamus see me, they treat me with respect. They call me 'friend.' We are equals."

When Elephant and Hippopotamus heard this boast, they laughed. "Does Turtle say we call him 'friend'? That is nonsense. We are much bigger and more powerful than Turtle. We do not call him 'friend.' We have no time to waste thinking of so small a creature."

The animals told Turtle what Elephant and Hippopotamus said. "So," said Turtle, "because they are so much bigger, they think they are so much better. But I will show them that I am their equal. Just wait and see. They will call me 'friend,' indeed they will!" And he set off down the path.

Soon Turtle found Elephant lying among the trees. Elephant was himself almost as big as the trees. But Turtle walked right up to him and shouted, "Hey! Wake up and pay your respects to your friend."

Elephant looked around to see who was speaking. Then he saw Turtle. "What do you want, you little thing of no importance?" he groaned.

"Is that any way to speak to your friend?" snapped Turtle.

"I am not your friend, Turtle," replied Elephant. "I have heard that you have been boasting that Hippopotamus and I call you 'friend.' You have been saying that you are our equal. But we do not call you 'friend.' And you are not our equal. You are a foolish little creature. Be off with you."

"Listen to me, Elephant," said Turtle. "Because I am so small, and you are so big, you think that you are greater. But I say we are equal. And I say, let us have a contest to prove it. I challenge you to a tug-of-war."

Elephant laughed so hard that the ground shook. "A tug-of-war with you?" he roared. "Turtle, don't be a stupid little creature. You would have no chance against me."

"So, what have you got to lose?" asked Turtle. Then he cut a very long vine and gave one end to Elephant. "You take this end. I will walk off with the other end. Then we will begin to pull. If you pull me down, you are greater. If I pull you down, I am greater. We will not stop to eat or sleep until one of us pulls the other down, or until the vine breaks. And if the vine breaks, we are equals, and you must call me 'friend.'"

Turtle took the other end of the long vine and walked far away until he came to the river. There was Hippopotamus splashing in the water.

"Hey, friend! Come out!" shouted Turtle. "I have something to say to you."

Hippopotamus came to the shore and snorted, "You are no friend of mine! You are a little good-for-nothing. Be off with you."

Then Turtle challenged Hippopotamus to a tug-of-war. "Take this vine," he said. "If you pull me down, you are greater. If I pull you down, I am greater. We will not stop to eat or sleep until one of us pulls the other down, or until the vine breaks. And if the vine breaks, we are equals, and you must call me 'friend.'"

"Turtle," said Hippopotamus, "I will do this only to stop your boasting, and to show you who is truly greater. Now go pick up your end of the vine and let us be done with it."

So Turtle walked till he came to the middle of the vine. He picked it up and gave it a very hard shake. Elephant felt this and started to tug. Hippopotamus felt the tug and started to tug back.

Elephant and Hippopotamus pulled with all their strength. The vine stretched tight. Turtle sat down on soft moss and watched the vine. It moved a few inches one way,  then a few inches the other way. But neither Elephant nor Hippopotamus could pull the other down.

Turtle munched on some mushrooms for a snack. Then he fell asleep. He awoke refreshed from his nap to see the vine still pulled tight. He yawned and stretched. Then he walked up to the vine and cut it with a sharp rock. At either end, Elephant and Hippopotamus crashed hard to the ground.

Turtle went to see Elephant first. Elephant was rubbing his head. "I bumped my head when the vine broke," moaned Elephant.

"Oh," said Turtle, "I am so sorry, my friend."

"Yes, we will call each other 'friend,'" said Elephant. "You are small but you are much stronger than I ever thought possible. We are equals."

Then Turtle went to see Hippopotamus, who was rubbing his leg. "So, Turtle," said Hippopotamus, "I see we are equals after all. Although I pulled with all my might, I could not pull you down. You amaze me, my little friend."

"Thank you, my friend," said Turtle.

And so it is that, whenever the animals hold a meeting, Turtle, Elephant, and Hippopotamus sit at the front and they call each other "friend." Now they rule as equals—but do you think they are equal?

Chipmunk and Bear

Long ago when animals could talk, a bear was walking along. Now it has always been said that bears think very highly of themselves. Since they are big and strong, they are certain that they are the most important of the animals.

As this bear went along turning over big logs with his paws to look for food to eat, he felt very sure of himself. "There is nothing I cannot do," said the bear.

"Is that so?" said a small voice. Bear looked down. There was a little chipmunk looking up at bear from its hole in the ground.

"Yes," Bear said, "that is true indeed." He reached out one huge paw and rolled over a big log. "Look at how easily I can do this. I am the strongest of all the animals. I can do anything. All the other animals fear me."

"Can you stop the sun from rising in the morning?" said the chipmunk.

Bear thought for a moment. "I have never tried that," he said. "Yes, I am sure I could stop the sun from rising."

"You are sure?" said Chipmunk.

"I am sure," said Bear. "Tomorrow morning the sun will not rise. I, Bear, have said so." Bear sat down facing the east to wait.

Behind him the sun set for the night and still he sat there. The chipmunk went into its hole and curled up in its snug little nest, chuckling about how foolish Bear was. All through the night Bear sat. Finally the first birds started their songs and the east glowed with the light that comes before the sun.

"The sun will not rise today," said Bear. He stared hard at the growing light. "The sun will not rise today."

However, the sun rose, just as it always had. Bear was very upset, but Chipmunk was delighted. He laughed and laughed. "Sun is stronger than Bear," said the chipmunk, twittering with laughter. Chipmunk was so amused that he came out of his hole and began running around in circles, singing this song:

> "The sun came up,
>   The sun came up.
>   Bear is angry,
>   But the sun came up."

While Bear sat there looking very unhappy, Chipmunk ran around and around, singing and laughing until he was so weak that he rolled over on his back. Then, quicker than the leap of a fish from a stream, Bear shot out one big paw and pinned him to the ground.

"Perhaps I cannot stop the sun from rising," said Bear, "but you will never see another sunrise."

"Oh, Bear," said the chipmunk, "oh, oh, oh, you are the strongest, you are the quickest, you are the best of all of the animals. I was only joking." But Bear did not move his paw.

"Oh, Bear," Chipmunk said, "you are right to kill me. I deserve to die. Just please let me say one last prayer to the Creator before you eat me."

"Say your prayer quickly," said Bear. "Your time to walk the Sky Road has come!"

"Oh, Bear," said Chipmunk, "I would like to die. But you are pressing down on me so hard I cannot breathe. I can hardly squeak. I do not have enough breath to say a prayer. If you would just lift your paw a little, just a little bit, then I could breathe. And I could say my last prayer to the Maker of all, to the one who made great, wise, powerful Bear and foolish, weak, little Chipmunk."

Bear lifted up his paw. He lifted it just a little bit. That little bit, though, was enough. Chipmunk squirmed free and ran for his hole as quickly as the blinking of an eye. Bear swung his paw at the little chipmunk as it darted away, but the very tips of his long claws scraped along Chipmunk's back, leaving three pale scars.

To this day, all chipmunks wear those scars as a reminder to them of what happens when one animal makes fun of another.

– An Iroquois tale retold by Joseph Bruchac

THE TIGER, THE BRAHMAN, AND THE JACKAL

1

Once upon a time in India, a Brahman was walking along the road. His mind was so filled with calm thoughts that he hardly noticed where he was going.

As he walked along in peace, he was startled by the sound of a most desperate growling, roaring, and snapping of teeth.

He looked up to see a tiger caught in a large cage. The tiger was biting at the bars in rage, but in vain.

When the tiger saw the Brahman, he cried out, "My holy friend, please let me out of this trap."

The kind Brahman began to open the trap but then stopped. "No," he said, "for I fear that if I release you, you will eat me. After all, it is in your nature."

"It is in my nature to be free!" replied the tiger. "I promise, if you release me, I will do you no harm. I will serve you forever!"

"A Brahman has no need of a servant," said the holy man. "And besides, once you are out of this cage, you are likely to forget your promises."

The Brahman turned and began to walk away. But then the tiger called out in a pitiful voice, "Would you leave me here to die? Is that the way of a holy man?"

At this, the Brahman stopped. Then he turned back and opened the door of the cage. In one bound the tiger popped out and grabbed the Brahman. "Thank you, my foolish friend," said the tiger. "And now, as I have been trapped for so long, and have grown very hungry, I must eat you!"

"Wait one minute!" cried the Brahman. "I gave you your freedom. Now, give me a chance for mine. If I can find three things that say you should let me go free, then will you let me go?"

"I will," said the tiger, "but be quick about it. I am hungry!"

So the Brahman turned to a nearby tree and asked, "Oh, tree! You saw me let this tiger out of the trap. Is it not right that the tiger should let me go free?"

But the tree replied, "Why do you complain? Look at me. I give shade to all who pass by, and how do they thank me? They tear off my branches to feed to their animals. Take what is coming to you—be a man!"

Then the Brahman asked the same question of a buffalo. The buffalo answered, "Do you expect the tiger to thank you for what you did? Don't be foolish. Look at me. For years, as long as I gave milk, people treated me kindly and fed me well. But now that I am old, they make me pull heavy loads and feed me stale scraps. You can't expect goodness in return for goodness."

The sad Brahman asked the road what he thought of the matter. The road answered, "My good sir, do you really expect thanks for your kindness? Look at me. All day long, people walk on me. And how do they thank me for this service? They spit on me and throw their trash on me."

"Alas!" cried the Brahman. "It appears I must be eaten."

2

Just as the Brahman turned to face the hungry tiger, a jackal walked up. "Oh good and holy man," said the jackal, "why do you look so sad on such a fine day?"

The Brahman told him all that had happened. He told how he had found the tiger trapped in the cage. He told how he had let the tiger go free. He explained how he asked the tree, buffalo, and road for their opinions. "And now," he sadly concluded, "it appears I must be eaten."

The jackal scratched his head and said with a puzzled look, "Would you please tell me the story again? I'm afraid I found it very confusing."

Once more the Brahman told what had happened. When he finished, the jackal said, "I am sorry to be so slow-witted, but I'm afraid I still don't understand. Let me see—the tiger was walking along and found the Brahman in the cage…."

"No!" roared the tiger. "Have you no brain at all? The Brahman was not in the cage. I was in the cage!"

"Oh, yes, of course," said the jackal. "I was in the cage and—oh, no, that's not quite right. Let me try again. The tiger was in the Brahman, and then the buffalo opened the tiger, and—oh, dear, I'm afraid I simply can't understand it!"

"You will understand," growled the tiger. "Now, listen carefully. I am the tiger. Do you see that?"

"Yes, my lord," said the jackal in a meek voice.

"And this man is the Brahman."

"Yes, my lord."

"And right here is the cage."

"Indeed, my lord."

"And I was in this cage—do you see?" said the tiger.

"Yes, my lord. I was—I mean, you were—I mean, the Brahman was—oh, dear, dear, just when it seems to make sense, I get all confused again!"

"What will it take to make you understand?" the tiger roared.

"Perhaps, my lord," said the jackal, "if we could start at the beginning, and if you would be so kind as to show me what happened. Now, the Brahman was in the cage…."

"NO!" shouted the tiger. "I was in the cage—like this!" He stepped inside the cage. "Now do you understand, you foolish jackal?"

"Indeed, my lord," said the jackal as he stepped forth and, with one quick movement, shut and locked the cage. "I understand perfectly!"

ANIMALS AND THEIR PEOPLE

CHARLIE AND TOPSY

1

Once there was a little boy named Charlie. He lived with his mother and daddy and auntie in a house in the city. A cat called Jane and Jane's kitten, whose name was Topsy, also lived in the house.

Charlie was a good boy and everybody liked him. Everybody, that is, except Jane the cat and Topsy the kitten. They did not like him at all.

This was very sad, because Charlie loved Jane and Topsy more than anything else in the world, excepting his mother, daddy, and auntie. He loved Jane and Topsy a thousand times more than his electric train set or even his enormous flashlight.

Yet Jane and Topsy ran away whenever they saw him coming. And what do you think was the reason?

The reason was this. Charlie liked that cat and kitten so much that he was never happy unless he was holding them tight in his arms and squeezing them all day long. Whenever he saw them running on their own four legs, he would grab them and squeeze them and bother them. Most of the time he grabbed Topsy because Topsy was little and couldn't run away so fast.

Again and again his mother and auntie said to him, "Charlie, put that kitten down! Don't you see that he doesn't want to be held all the time? Let him run around and play. You wouldn't like it if we were to carry you around all day and hug you and squeeze you. Just run around and let him chase you. A kitten loves to run and scamper and jump, but he does not like to be picked up and carried all the time."

But Charlie would not listen. He picked the kitten up all the time and he would not let him run around at all. He bothered and teased him all day long. Topsy called out, "Meow, meow," but Charlie paid no attention. He just went on squeezing and teasing the poor kitten.

2

One day Charlie was walking around in the yard looking for Topsy. Topsy was hiding in the bushes near the fence. He was hiding because he did not want to be grabbed and hugged and squeezed.

Charlie saw Topsy and reached out his hand to grab the kitten. But suddenly, a great big hand grabbed

Charlie! Yes, a great big hand grabbed him by his trousers and lifted him clear off the ground and over the fence. And a great big voice called out, "Oooo-eee! What a darling little teeny-tiny creature!"

Charlie squirmed around to see what was holding him. It was a giant little girl. She had brown hair tied with a red bow, and all in all she was a very pretty girl—and very big, more than twice as big as Charlie's mother, daddy, or auntie.

She looked at Charlie and again she squealed, "Oooo-eee! You darling little thing! I'm going to take you home right this minute." She began to run, still holding Charlie by his trousers. She ran so fast that his head bobbed up and down.

Charlie called out, "Put me down! Put me down!" But the giant little girl paid no attention at all.

"Mama! Mama!" she cried. Look what I found. It's a darling, teeny little doll. And it's alive, Mama! It walks and it talks!"

"That's nice, dear," said the girl's mama. "Take care not to tease it or drag it about."

But the girl paid no attention. She poked Charlie in the middle of his back and said, "Walk. Walk!"

"Ouch! Don't do that!" cried Charlie.

Then she lifted Charlie high in the air and kissed him and squeezed him and hugged him till Charlie thought he could not breathe. And he did not like it one bit.

The girl ran out of the room but came right back with an enormous piece of cake. She stuffed a piece into Charlie's face. "Look, Mama," she cried, "he can eat like a real live person. Isn't he cute? Do you want some more, little person?"

Charlie realized that he was in fact very hungry, so he reached for the cake. But the girl held it just out of his reach. When he jumped for it, she pulled it away and laughed.

"Mama," called the girl, "may I go over and show him to Sophie? Please, Mama, please?"

The girl's mama said she might go and show Charlie to Sophie, but she mustn't stay long. Charlie kicked and cried out, "I want to go home!" But the girl paid no attention. She picked him up and stuffed him in her pocket and started to run to show Sophie.

There were many things in the girl's pocket—pencils, a nail, and some sharp pebbles. As she ran, they bumped and knocked poor Charlie.

But there was one more thing in the girl's pocket—a hole! The next thing Charlie knew, he fell through the hole and landed with a thump in the road. The girl ran on, and she never knew till she got to Sophie's house that she had lost Charlie through the hole in her pocket.

3

As for Charlie, you can guess how fast he ran! He ran and ran and never stopped till he got home. He rushed into the living room where his mother and auntie were sitting. Jane and Topsy were there as well. When they saw Charlie, they scurried behind the bookcase.

"Oh, Mother! Oh, Auntie!" said Charlie, gasping for breath. "A terrible little giant girl caught me, and hugged me and teased me, and I fell through a hole in her pocket, and—and here I am!"

"Such a lively imagination," said Charlie's auntie to his mother.

"Oh, Mother," cried Charlie, "I don't think Jane and Topsy will ever love me. I squeezed them and carried them about and bothered them so!"

Then his auntie said, "Cheer up, Charlie. Go to my sewing basket. I'll show you how to make friends with Jane and Topsy."

She gave Charlie a ball of yarn and fixed it so that it would not unwind. Then she told Charlie to roll it round and round in front of the bookcase. Soon a little gray paw came out, then another, and another, and soon Topsy was dancing around the room, chasing the ball of yarn.

Sometimes he danced on all four legs, sometimes on his two back ones. Sometimes he jumped sideways, and sometimes he jumped straight up in the air. He seemed to be having such a good time that Jane came out from her hiding place to join the fun.

Never again did Charlie grab hold of Topsy or Jane against their will. Never again did he carry Topsy around and pay no attention when the kitten cried out, "Meow, meow!"

From that day to this, Charlie played nicely with Topsy and did the things the kitten liked best. And now Topsy loves Charlie more than anyone else and follows him everywhere.

MOUFFLU

1

Lolo and Moufflu were the best of friends. Moufflu was the biggest and whitest poodle in the city of Florence, and Lolo was a little lame boy, his master. They lived with Lolo's mother and brothers and sisters under the shadow of a great cathedral.

They were all happy and merry, except when they did not have enough to eat, which was very often, for they were poor. Lolo's mother worked, and his brothers and sisters worked, and Lolo worked as much as he could. But as he was lame, most of the time he liked to sit by the door of the cathedral where people came and went.

One morning, as he sat on the steps in the sunshine, a strange gentleman stopped in front of him.

" What a pretty dog you have, my boy!" he said kindly.

"Moufflu is beautiful," said Lolo with pride. "You should see him on Sundays just after he is washed."

"How old is your dog?"

"Three years old."

"Does he do any tricks?"

"Does he?" cried Lolo. "Why, Moufflu can do anything! Would you like to see him do his tricks?"

"Very much," said the gentleman.

So Moufflu walked on two legs, danced and played dead, begged and made a wheelbarrow of himself, and did everything else you could imagine.

The strange gentleman clapped his hands. "Your dog is very clever," he said. "Would you be willing to bring him to please a sick child I have at home?"

Lolo smiled and said he would. The man told him to come to a great hotel, and dropped two francs into Lolo's hand. "Come this afternoon," he said.

Lolo hurried home with the coins clasped tight in his hand.

"All because Moufflu did his tricks!" he cried as he gave the money to his mother. "Now you can get the shoes you need, and the coffee you miss so much every morning, and—oh, almost everything!" Two francs seemed a great deal of money to Lolo.

2

That afternoon Lolo and Moufflu trotted to the great hotel. They were shown into a beautiful room with gilded walls and velvet furniture.

There was the strange gentleman, and there on a couch lay a pale little boy. He spoke a strange language that Lolo could not understand, but from the way he clapped his hands, Lolo knew that he liked Moufflu's tricks.

The boy gave them crackers and cakes, which Lolo and Moufflu ate with great delight. And when at last the man sent them away, he put five francs into Lolo's hand.

As they trotted home, Lolo thought how fine it would be if a strange gentleman with a sick little boy came every day to their cathedral.

Alas for Lolo! He had not understood the sick child's cries as he and Moufflu had left the room. "I want the dog! I will have the dog! I want him!" the child had cried.

The next day the strange gentleman came to Lolo's home. He said that the sick child wanted the dog and was heartbroken when Moufflu was taken away. The man said that they would pay a thousand francs. Would they sell the dog?

The poor mother looked at the thousand francs he held out, and then at Moufflu. Surely a dog was not worth that! Lolo loved him, to be sure, but a dog was a dog, and the children were hungry, and there was nothing in the cupboard. At last she took the money, and the man carried Moufflu away.

That night when Lolo came home, no Moufflu ran to meet him.

"Moufflu! Moufflu!" he cried in a frightened voice. "Where is Moufflu?"

When they told him he burst into tears.

The next day he was very ill, and the next, and the next. All the time he kept calling for Moufflu.

The old doctor shook his head. "What is this Moufflu the boy calls for?" he asked. "Bring him that. It is the only thing that can help him."

The poor mother was heartbroken. She had never known that Lolo loved the dog so much.

She would gladly have brought Moufflu back, but she could not. When they asked for the strange gentleman at the hotel, they were told that he had gone away. The servants shook their heads. They did not know where he had gone.

3

When they were all beginning to think that Lolo would never get better, Moufflu came back. Thin and dirty and caked with mud, he came dashing up the stairs one night at sunset. He was just as happy to see them as they were to see him. It seemed as if he would knock himself over wagging his tail.

From that hour Lolo began to get better. He would hardly let the dog out of his sight. Ten days went by, and still his mother did not dare tell him that Moufflu did not belong to them now.

No one knew where the dog had come from. Lolo's brother, Tasso, went to the hotel to look for the strange gentleman, but he was not there.

Each day they expected someone to come for Moufflu. The mother wanted to buy him back with the thousand francs, which she had carefully saved. But what if the strange gentleman would not sell him? She did not dare to think of it.

At last one day when Tasso went to the hotel, he was told that the gentleman had returned. He was taken to the same room where Lolo had gone, and there he found the gentleman and the little boy.

He told them the whole story—how sick Lolo had been, how he had missed Moufflu, and how the dog had come back. He gave the thousand francs to the man and begged him to sell the dog. They would be glad to train another little dog for the boy, he said.

The man was silent a moment. Then he said, "He came alone all the way from Rome. He is a wonderful dog."

He turned to the child. "Did you understand?" he asked.

"Yes! Yes!" cried the child. "Let the little boy have Moufflu, Father. Please!"

The gentleman smiled and gave the money back to Tasso. "This is to pay for the new dog," he said. Tasso was so surprised and happy that he could hardly thank the kind man.

So Moufflu and Lolo grew strong and well and happy again. In the shadow of the cathedral, they trained another dog. The other little boy said he was just as good a dog as Moufflu, but Lolo knew better.

– Adapted from a story by Louise de la Ramée

BLACK BEAUTY

1

The first place that I can well remember was a large, pleasant meadow. There were six young colts in the meadow besides my mother and me. They were much older than I was. Some of them were nearly as large as grown-up horses.

My master would not sell me till I was four years old. He said colts ought not to work like horses until they were quite grown up.

When I was four years old, Squire Gordon came to look at me. He examined my eyes, my mouth, and my legs. Then I had to walk, trot, and gallop for him.

He seemed to like me and said, "When he has been broken in, he will do very well."

As everyone may not know what breaking in is, I shall describe it. I had, of course, been used to being led about in the fields by a halter. Now, however, I must have a bit and a bridle.

My master gave me some oats, as usual, and after much coaxing he put the bit in my mouth and the bridle on my head. It was most unpleasant.

A great piece of cold, hard steel was pushed into my mouth, between my teeth, and over my tongue. Then straps were fastened over my nose and chin, so that I could not get rid of the hard thing.

Next came the saddle, but that was not half so bad. My master put it on my back very gently, while old Daniel held my head. Then I had a few oats, and he led me about the field.

This he did every day, until I began to look for the oats and the saddle.

At length, one morning, my master got on my back and rode me around the meadow. It certainly did feel queer, but I was proud to carry my master and soon grew used to the feeling.

After that, I was taken to the blacksmith's to be shod. My master went with me and talked to me so that I should not be frightened. The blacksmith took my feet, one after the other, and cut away some of the hoof.

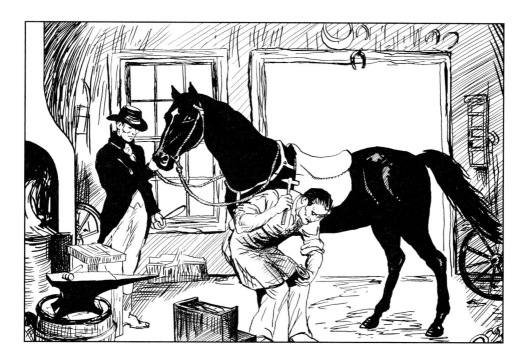

The cutting did not hurt at all. I stood on three legs and let the smith hold one foot in his hand. Then he took the heavy iron shoes and nailed them to my feet.

That did not hurt either, but the shoes made my feet feel very stiff and heavy. Later I found that these shoes kept my feet from being hurt by the stony roads.

When my master was ready to teach me to draw the carriage, there were more new things to wear. I shall not name all of them.

The worst of these was the stiff little strap called the crupper. That went under my tail. I hated it. To have my long tail doubled up and poked through that strap was as bad as the bit.

I must not forget one important part of my training. My master sent me for two weeks to a meadow near a railroad track. Here were some sheep and cows, and I was turned in among them.

I shall never forget the first train that ran by. I was feeding quietly when I heard a strange sound. Before I knew it, a long, black train flew by. I turned and galloped to the other side of the meadow and stood there snorting with fear. The cows, however, went on eating and hardly raised their heads.

For the first few days I could not eat in peace because of these trains. Later I found they never came into the fields or hurt me in any way. Then I was less frightened, and soon I paid no more attention than the cows did.

As the days passed, I grew more and more used to my work. My coat was brushed every day until it shone like satin, and my mane and tail were smooth and clean.

In time I became used to everything and could do my work as well as my mother. In fact, my master often drove me in double harness with my mother. She was steady and could teach me much.

She told me the better I behaved, the better I should be treated, and that it was wisest always to do my best to please my master. "But," said she, "there are a great many kinds of men. There are good, thoughtful men like our master, which any horse may be proud to serve. And there are bad, cruel men, who never ought to have a horse or dog to call their own. And there are a great many foolish men, who never trouble themselves to think; these spoil more horses than all. I hope you will fall into good hands, but a horse never knows who may buy him. It is all a chance for us. But still I say, do your best wherever it is, and keep up your good name."

At last, early in May, Squire Gordon sent a man to bring me to his home at Birtwick Park. My master came to the stable to say goodbye. I put my nose in his hand, and he patted my neck.

"Goodbye," he said. "Be a good horse and always do your best."

Then I was led out of the stable and away from my first home.

2

One night I had eaten my hay and I was lying on my straw asleep. Suddenly I was roused by the loud ringing of the stable bell. I heard the coachman, John Manly, open the door of his cottage near my stable. Then I heard the sound of his feet running down to the house.

He was back again in no time. He unlocked the stable door and called out, "Wake up, Beauty! You must go now, if ever you did."

Almost before I could think, he had the saddle on my back and the bridle on my head. He ran for his coat and took me at a quick trot to the front door of the house. Squire Gordon stood there with a lamp in his hand.

"Now, John," he said, "ride for your life—that is, for the life of your mistress. Give this note to Dr. White, and be back as soon as you can."

John said, "Yes, sir," and was on my back in an instant.

The gardener, who lived near the gate, had heard the bell ring. He had the gate open, and away we went, through the park and the village, till we came to the tollgate.

John called very loud and thumped on the door. The man was soon out and flung open the gate.

"Now," said John, "keep the gate open for the doctor. Here is the money."

There lay before us a long piece of level road. John said to me, "Now, Beauty, do your best," and so I did. I wanted neither whip nor spur. For two miles I galloped as fast as I could lay my feet to the ground.

When we came to the bridge, John pulled me up a little and patted my neck. He would have let me go slower, but I was off again, as fast as before. On and on we went, until, at the end of eight miles, we came to the town.

It was all quite still, except for the clatter of my feet on the stones. Everybody was asleep. The church clock struck three as we drew up at Dr. White's door.

John rang the bell twice and then knocked at the door like thunder. A window opened, and Dr. White put his head out.

"What do you want?" he called.

"Mrs. Gordon is very sick. Master thinks she will die if you do not get there. Here is a note."

The doctor shut the window and was soon at the door.

"The worst of it is that my horse has been out all day and is very tired," he said. "Can I have your horse?"

"He has come at a gallop nearly all the way, sir, but I think my master would be willing," said John.

"All right," said the doctor, "I will soon be ready."

The doctor came out with his riding-whip.

"You need not take that, sir," said John. "Black Beauty will go till he drops. Take care of him, sir, if you can. I should not like any harm to come to him."

"No, no, John," said the doctor, "I hope not." And in a minute we had left John far behind.

I shall not tell you about our way back. The doctor was a heavier man than John, and not so good a rider. However, I did my best. The man at the tollgate had it open, and soon we were in the park.

My master was at the door, for he had heard us coming. The doctor went into the house with him, and Joe, the new stable boy, led me to the stable.

I was glad to get home. My legs shook under me and I could only stand and pant. Joe was young and as yet he knew little about horses. I am sure he did the best he knew.

He rubbed my legs and chest, but he did not put my warm cloth on me. He thought I was hot so I should not like it. Then he gave me cold water and some hay and corn. Thinking he had done right, he went away.

Soon I began to shake and tremble with cold. Oh, how I wished for my warm cloth! I wished for John, too, but he had eight miles to walk.

After a long while I heard him at the door, and I gave a low moan.

He was at my side in a moment. I could not tell him how I felt, but he seemed to understand. He covered me with two or three warm cloths and then ran to the house for hot water. He made me some warm gruel, which I drank, and after that I think I must have gone to sleep.

I do not know how long I was ill. John nursed me night and day. He would get up two or three times in the night to come to me. My master, too, often came to see me. "My poor Beauty," he said one day, "my good horse, you saved your mistress's life, Beauty; yes, you saved her life."

I was very glad to hear that. It seems the doctor had said if we had been a little longer, my mistress would have died.

John told my master he never saw a horse go so fast in his life. He said it seemed as if the horse knew what was the matter. Of course I did. At least I knew that John and I must go at the top of our speed, and that it was for the sake of the mistress.

– Adapted from the novel by Anna Sewell

TALES OF THE BROTHERS GRIMM

THE BROTHERS WHO LOVED
FAIRY TALES

This is a true story about two brothers who grew up to love fairy tales.

Long ago in Germany there lived a man and his wife and their many children. The family did not have a lot of money, but they had enough to put food on the table and a roof over their heads.

The two oldest boys, Jacob and Wilhelm Grimm, were the best of friends. They walked through the woods together. They collected rocks. They teased and played with their younger brothers and sister.

But what they liked most was listening to stories. And most of all they loved fairy tales. Jacob and Wilhelm were always asking people to tell them stories.

When Jacob was 11 and Wilhelm was 10, their father died. Their mother had her hands full with so many children, so she sent the two oldest boys to live with an aunt.

Jacob and Wilhelm went to school together. When they weren't studying, they played games in the Black Forest.

The dark forest, with its tall fir trees and thick shadows, was the perfect place to act out the fairy tales they knew by heart.

The years passed and the boys grew into men. Then, when Jacob was 23 years old and Wilhelm a year younger, their mother died. Jacob returned home to take care of his four younger brothers and sister.

Jacob and Wilhelm had different jobs, but they both ended up working for a big library. Even though they weren't children anymore, they still loved fairy tales. In the library they looked for books with fairy tales, but they couldn't find any.

And so Jacob and Wilhelm decided to write a book of their own. They decided to fill their book with the wonderful stories they had heard and acted out when they were boys.

The brothers didn't make up new stories. Instead, they wrote down the tales they heard while growing up. They put these stories into a book and called it *Children's and Household Tales*.

Many people loved the book. They came to visit the brothers and tell them many more wonderful stories from their own childhood days.

Jacob and Wilhelm added more stories to their book. The brothers became famous for the stories they collected. There is even a statue of the brothers in the town in Germany where they lived much of their life.

People around the world still enjoy the stories that the Brothers Grimm collected, and they often call these stories "Grimm's fairy tales."

Do you know any of these Grimm's fairy tales?

Cinderella
Sleeping Beauty
Hansel and Gretel
Snow White and the Seven Dwarfs
Rapunzel
Rumpelstiltskin
Little Red Riding Hood

Snow White and Rose Red

1

Once upon a time there lived in a cottage near a wood a poor widow. In the garden in front of her house grew two rosebushes, one of which bore white roses and the other red. The widow had two little girls who were so like the rosebushes that she named one girl Snow White and the other Rose Red.

Snow White was quiet and gentle. She used to stay at home with her mother, help her with the housework, and read to her after the work was done. Rose Red liked to run about the fields and look for birds and flowers.

The two children were very fond of each other, and when out walking always went hand in hand. Snow White would say, "We will never leave each other," while her sister would answer, "No, never so long as we live."

The children often went to the wood to pick berries. Not a living thing ever did them any harm. All the animals were quite friendly with them. The birds sang for them in trees. The rabbits ate leaves out of their hands. Even the deer would not run from them. Sometimes they would stay in the forest all night, and still their mother knew there was no cause for fear.

One morning, after the sisters had been sleeping all night in a soft bed of moss, they opened their eyes and saw near them a beautiful little child, whose clothes were white and shining. When he saw that they were awake, he smiled at them kindly and then seemed to go away in a mist. They looked around and found that they had been sleeping on the edge of a dark, deep hole, into which they would surely have fallen had they moved during the night. Their mother said that the child they saw must have been one of the angels who watch over all good children.

The little girls kept their mother's house so neat and clean that there was never a speck of dust to be found. Each morning in summer, Rose Red picked fresh flowers to place by her mother's bed. In winter, Snow White made the fire, filled the teakettle, and placed it over the bright blaze.

In the evening, when the snow was falling and the door closed and locked, Snow White and Rose Red would take seats around the fire in the bright little room and knit their stockings, while their mother read to them out of some good book.

One evening there came a rap at the door, and the mother said, "Rose Red, open the door quickly. Someone may be lost in the snow."

So Rose Red unlocked the door, and in came a great, black bear.

At first they were all very much afraid, until the bear began to speak. "Do not fear. I will not hurt you," said the bear. "I only wish to warm myself by the fire, for my paws are nearly frozen."

"Poor bear," cried the mother, "come and lie down by the fire, but take care not to burn your coat of fur."

Then she called out, "Snow White and Rose Red, come closer! This is a good bear. He will not hurt you." So they both came up by the fire, and the bear said, "Dear children, will you please sweep the snow from my fur?"

They took the broom and brushed the bear's fur until it was quite smooth. Then the huge fellow lay down at full length before the warm fire. In a short time the children had lost all fear of him. They jumped upon his back, rolled over him on to the floor, and pulled his thick fur. All this the bear did not mind in the least.

When bedtime came, the mother said to him, "You may stay here by the fire all night if you like, as it is too cold for you to try to go home."

In the morning, when all were up, the two children opened the door, and the bear trotted off into the wood. After this he came every evening, always at the same time. He would lie down in front of the fire and let the children play with him as much as they pleased. At last they grew so used to him that no one thought of locking the door until the big black bear had come in.

So the winter passed. Then the grass began to grow, the buds began to swell, and the birds began to sing. Spring had come.

One morning the bear said to Snow White, "I shall be gone all summer, and you will not see me again until winter comes."

"Where are you going, dear bear?" asked Snow White.

"I must go into the forest," he answered, "to hide my gold from the wicked dwarfs. While winter is here and the ground is frozen hard, they cannot find it. But when the snow is gone and the sun has warmed the earth, it is easy for them to dig up my gold. Once they have stolen anything, it is hard to get it back again."

Snow White felt very sorry when the bear said goodbye. As he went out of the door, the latch caught his fur and tore off a piece. Snow White thought she saw something shine like gold under his skin, but she was not sure, for the bear went away quickly and was soon lost to sight in the forest.

One day the mother sent her children into the forest to pick up wood. While walking along hand in hand, they came upon a large tree that had fallen to the ground. Snow White thought she saw something jumping up and down on the other side of the trunk. When they came

nearer, they found that a little dwarf with a dried-up face had caught his long beard in a crack of the tree.

The dwarf was jumping about like a puppy at the end of a leash, but he could not get free. He looked at the children with his red, fiery eyes, and cried, "What are you standing there for? Why don't you help me out?"

"Poor little man!" said Rose Red. "How did this happen?"

"You stupid goose!" he cried. "I was trying to split the tree, but as I drove in my ax, it slipped out, and the tree closed so quickly that I caught my long white beard in it. Now why don't you do something?"

In spite of his cross words and mean looks, the children were willing to help him. They tried to pull out his beard, but the tree held it fast.

"Ah, I know what to do," cried Snow White. She quickly took her scissors out of her pocket and cut off the dwarf's beard close to the trunk of the tree. No sooner was the ill-tempered fellow free than he grabbed a bag of gold lying among the roots. Then he ran off without even thanking the children.

A short time after this, Snow White and Rose Red went out to catch some fish for dinner. When they came to the edge of the stream, they saw something like a great grasshopper hopping about on the bank. As they ran up, they found that it was the little old dwarf.

"What is the matter?" asked Rose Red. "Why are you jumping up and down?"

"Do you think I am a dunce?" he cried. "Don't you see that I have caught a big fish, and that he has almost dragged me into the water?"

Then the children saw that the long beard of the dwarf was tangled in his line, and that the fish had indeed almost dragged him into the water. They caught hold of him and pulled him back just in time. His long beard was so wound up in the line that, in spite of all they could do, Snow White had to take out her little scissors and cut it off again. This time only a little piece of the beard was left.

When the dwarf saw this, he was in a great rage. "Why did you cut my beard off so short?" he cried. "Am I to lose all that I have at your hands? I shall not dare to show my face!" While he continued to talk in this way, he picked up a bag of pearls, which he had hidden in a tuft of grass, and ran quickly away.

A few days later, the mother sent her two children to town to buy some ribbon and thread. Their path led across a field, and soon Snow White saw a large bird flying round and round. At last he dropped to the ground, and at the same time they heard cries and shouts as if someone were being killed.

The children ran up to the place and found that a fierce bird had caught the dwarf in its claws and was trying to fly away with him. The children did all they could to help the little man. They pulled and tugged so hard that at last the bird let go and flew off to the wood.

The dwarf at once began to scold and rage. "Why did you hold me so tight?" he cried. "You have pulled my new coat nearly off my back, you nasty children."

Then he picked up his bag of diamonds and slipped away among the rocks. The little girls did not mind what he said in the least, but went on to town to buy the things for their mother.

On their way back, as they were crossing the same field, they came again upon the dwarf, who was counting his diamonds in the shade of a big rock. The diamonds flashed and sparkled with such beautiful colors that the children could not take their eyes from them.

"Why are you standing there?" cried the dwarf, his face quite red with rage. Just then they heard a growl, and a huge black bear walked in upon them.

The dwarf sprang up in a great fright, but he could not run, for the bear stood right in his way. Then he cried out and began to beg, "Dear Mr. Bear, spare my life! I will give you all my gold, my pearls, and my diamonds, if you will only spare my life. See, I am nothing but a mouthful. But those two fat young girls will make you a good meal. Just eat them instead of me."

Without a word, the bear lifted his great paw. With one swift stroke, he sent the dwarf flying through the air, never to return again.

The children started to run away, but the bear called out to them: "Snow White, Rose Red, don't be afraid! Wait, and I will go home with you."

Then they knew his voice, and stood still. But as he came toward them, what did they see? All at once the bearskin fell off, and out stepped a young man, with beautiful clothes and a smiling face.

"I am a king's son," he said, "and that wicked dwarf, after robbing me of nearly all my gold, cast a spell that changed me into a bear. I have not been able to catch the dwarf until today. Now I am free at last, and I am glad to be a bear no longer."

Not many years after, Snow White married the prince, and Rose Red married his brother. Their mother took the two rosebushes and planted them in the garden of the king's castle, and every year they bore the same beautiful red and white roses.

THE HOUSE IN THE FOREST

1

There was once a poor woodcutter who lived with his wife and two daughters near a lonely forest.

One morning he said to his wife, "Let Anne bring some dinner to me in the forest today. I will take a bag of grain with me and drop the seeds on the path. Anne can look for the grain and then she will know where to find me."

Just before noon Anne set out with a bowl of soup for her father. But as the sparrows and blackbirds had picked up the grain long before, she could not find the path.

She went on and on until the sun sank out of sight. It became very dark, and the owls hooted, and she began to cry.

At last Anne saw a light through the trees. "There must be some people there who will give me shelter," she said to herself.

She walked on till she came to a little house with light shining through its windows. She knocked loudly at the door, and a voice called, "Come in."

When she opened the door, she saw an old, white-haired man sitting at the table. Beside the fireplace sat three animals—a hen, a cock, and a cow.

Anne told her story to the old man and begged for shelter for the night. The man said,

> "Pretty little hen,
>   Pretty little cock,
>   And pretty brindled cow,
>   What do you say to that?"

"Duks," answered the animals. That must have meant, "We are willing," for the old man said, "Here you shall have shelter and food. There is enough to spare. Now, will you go to the kitchen and cook our supper?"

Anne cooked a good supper, but she never thought of the animals. As soon as she had carried the dishes to the table, she sat down and ate all she wanted.

After supper she said, "Now I am tired. Where can I sleep?"

The animals replied,

> "You have eaten with him,
>   You have drunk with him,
>   But you've had no thought for us.
>   So now find out for yourself
>   Where you can pass the night."

Anne ran upstairs and found a little room all ready for her. But as soon as she was sound asleep, a trapdoor opened. Down dropped her bed into the cellar!

2

Late that night the woodcutter came home and scolded his wife for leaving him hungry all day.

"It's not my fault," she replied. "Anne went out with your dinner. She must be lost, but she is sure to come back tomorrow."

The next day the woodcutter was up before dawn. "Let Rose bring my dinner into the forest today," said he. "She has always been a good child. She will stay in the right path and not run after every wild bee, as her sister did."

"Oh dear," said his wife. "I'm afraid she will get lost, too."

"No, no," replied the woodcutter. "She will not get lost. I will take some beans with me today and scatter them about. They are large, so she will be sure to see them."

But when Rose went out with her basket on her arm, the doves had already eaten all the beans and she did not know which way to turn. She walked on and on, full of sorrow as she thought how hungry her father would be.

At last when it grew dark, she came to the little house in the forest. She knocked gently and a voice called, "Come in."

"Please may I stay here till morning?" asked Rose.

The old, white-haired man turned to his animals and said,

> "Pretty little hen,
> Pretty little cock,
> And pretty brindled cow,
> What do you say to that?"

"*Duks*," said they.

"Yes," said the old man, "you shall have shelter and food. There is enough to spare."

Rose thanked him, and then she went over to the cock and the hen and stroked their smooth feathers with her hand, and she patted the brindled cow between the horns.

When she had cooked some soup and had placed the bowl on the table, she said, "Are the good animals to have nothing? Let me feed them now."

So she brought some grain for the cock and the hen and a whole armful of sweet-smelling hay for the cow. "I hope you will like it, dear animals," said she. "You shall have fresh water to drink, too, for I'm sure you are thirsty."

She brought a bucketful of water, and the cock and the hen and the brindled cow each took a long drink.

When the animals were fed, Rose sat down at the table and ate what was left.

It was not long before the cock and the hen began to put their heads under their wings, and the cow began to blink her eyes.

"May I go to bed now?" asked Rose.

The white-haired man said,

> " Pretty little hen,
> Pretty little cock,
> And pretty brindled cow,
> What do you say to that?"

The animals answered,

> " You have eaten with us,
>   You have drunk with us,
>   And you've had kind thoughts for all;
>   So now we wish you good night."

Rose went upstairs and found a little room all ready for her. She was soon fast asleep.

At midnight a great noise waked her. The doors slammed against the walls, and there was a crash as if the whole roof had fallen in.

Then all became still. Rose found that she was not hurt, so she went to sleep again.

3

The next morning when Rose woke up, she rubbed her eyes and looked all around. She was lying in a large room. The walls were covered with soft, white silk and golden flowers. The bed was of ivory and velvet, and on a chair beside it was a pair of slippers all shining with diamonds. Rose was sure she was dreaming.

Three servants came to her and asked what orders she would like to give.

"Oh dear," she said, "I'm afraid it is very late. I must get up at once and make some soup for the old man, and then I will feed the hen and the cock and the brindled cow."

When she looked for the old man, she found only a stranger, young and handsome.

He said to her, "I am a king's son. A witch changed me into a white-haired man and made me live in this forest. I have been all alone except for my three servants, who were changed to a cock, a hen, and a brindled cow.

"The spell could not be broken until a girl came to us who was full of love for animals as well as men. It is you who have set us free. At midnight the spell was broken, and the old house in the forest was changed into my royal palace. I hope you will stay here with me and be my wife."

Rose said that she would, and then the prince ordered one of his servants to bring her father and mother to the marriage feast.

"Can we not find my sister, too?" asked Rose. "She was lost in the forest yesterday."

"She is here now, locked in the cellar," replied the prince. "She must go back to the forest to stay until she learns to be kind to all creatures. Then she may come to live with us."

MOTHER FROST

1

There was once a widow who had two daughters. One was very kind and a great help about the house, while the other was mean and idle. The mother loved the mean one best, for she was her own child. She cared so little for the other daughter, who was her stepchild, that she made her do all of the hard work. Every day the poor girl walked to the spring, where she sat at a spinning wheel. She would spin and spin till her fingers bled.

One day when the poor girl could spin no longer, she tried to wash the spindle in the water of the spring. But the spindle fell out of her hand and sank to the bottom. With tears in her eyes, she ran and told her stepmother what she had done.

The stepmother was so angry that she said, "Since you have let the spindle fall into the spring, you must go in and get it out."

The maiden went back to the spring to look for her spindle. She leaned so far over the edge of the spring that she fell in and sank down, down to the very bottom.

When the poor girl first awoke, she could not think what had happened. As she came to herself, she found that she was in a beautiful field, on which the sun shone brightly and where hundreds of wild flowers grew.

She walked a long way across the field till she came to a baker's oven, full of new bread. The loaves cried to her, "Oh, pull us out! Pull us out, or we shall burn!"

"Ah, that would be a pity!" cried the maiden, and stepping up, she pulled all the sweet brown loaves out of the oven.

As she walked along, she soon came to a tree full of apples. The tree cried, "Shake me! Shake me! My apples are all quite ripe."

"If that is your wish, then shake you I shall," replied the kind-hearted girl. She shook the tree again and again. Then she picked up the apples one by one and piled them in a great heap.

At last she came to a small house. In the doorway sat an old woman with such large teeth that it made the girl feel quite afraid of her. She turned to run away, but the

old woman cried, "What do you fear, my child? Come in, and live here with me. If you will do the work about the house, I will be very kind to you. You must take care to make my bed well, and to shake it and pound it, so that the feathers will fly about. Then down in the world they will say that it snows, for I am Mother Frost."

The old woman spoke so kindly that she quite won the little girl's heart. And so the girl said she would gladly stay and work for her.

The girl did everything well. Each day she shook the bed until it was soft and nice, so that the feathers might fly down like snowflakes. Her life with Mother Frost was a happy one. She had plenty to eat and drink, and never once heard an angry word.

After she had stayed a long, long time with the kind old woman, she began to feel lonely and wished to go home. She was indeed quite homesick. She could not help it, though her life with Mother Frost had been very happy.

When she could stand it no longer, she said, "Dear Mother Frost, you have been very kind to me, but I feel in my heart that I cannot stay here any longer. I must go back to my own friends."

"It is right that you should wish to go home," said Mother Frost. "As you have worked for me so well, I will show you the way myself."

So she took the maiden by the hand and led her to a broad gateway. The gate was open, and as the young girl walked through, a shower of gold fell over her and hung to her clothes, so that she was dressed in gold from head to foot.

"That is your pay for having worked so hard," said the old woman. And as she spoke, she put into the maiden's hand the spindle that had fallen into the spring.

2

When the great gate closed, the girl found herself once more in the world, not far from her stepmother's house. It seemed as if very little time had passed since she left. As she came into the farmyard, a cock crowed loudly, "Cock-a-doodle-doo! Our golden lady has come home, I see."

When the stepmother saw the maiden, she started to scold. But when she saw her golden dress, she treated her kindly. As soon as the girl explained how the gold had fallen upon her, the stepmother could hardly wait to have her own child try her luck in the same way.

This time she made the idle daughter go to the spring and spin. But the lazy girl, who wished for riches without working, did not spin fast enough to make her fingers bleed. So she put her hand into the thorn bushes and pricked her finger, until at last a few drops of blood stained the spindle. At once she let it drop into the water, then sprang in after it herself.

Just as her sister had done, the mean girl found herself in a beautiful field, and walked along same path till she came to the baker's oven.

She heard the loaves cry, "Oh, pull us out! Pull us out, or we shall burn!"

But the lazy girl answered, "I will not do it. I do not want to soil my hands in your dirty oven."

And so she walked on till she came to the apple tree. "Shake me! Shake me!" it cried. "My apples are all quite ripe."

"I will not do it," answered the girl, "for some of your apples might fall on my head." As she spoke, she walked lazily on.

When at last the girl stood before the door of Mother Frost's house, she had no fear of the great teeth, for her sister had told her all about them. So she walked right up to the old woman and offered to be her servant.

For a whole day the girl was very busy and did everything that she was told to do. But on the second day, she began to be lazy, and on the third day, she was still worse. She would not get up in the morning. The bed was never made or shaken so the feathers could fly about. At last Mother Frost grew quite tired of her and told her that she must go away.

The lazy girl was indeed glad to go, for she thought only of the golden shower that was sure to come when Mother Frost led her to the gate. But as she passed under the gate, a large kettleful of black pitch poured out upon her.

"That is what you get for your work," said the old woman as she firmly shut the gate.

So the idle girl walked home all covered with thick, sticky pitch. As she went into the farmyard, the cock cried out, "Cock-a-doodle-doo! Our sticky young lady has come home, I see."

The pitch stuck fast to the girl's clothes and hair. And, try as she might, she could never get it off, for as long as she lived.

GREEK AND ROMAN MYTHS

MOUNT OLYMPUS AND ITS INHABITANTS

1

The ancient Greeks were a wonderful people. They lived on a sunny peninsula in southern Europe, with the Mediterranean Sea always near them.

Their minds were filled with poetry. They imagined wonderful beings in every spot, belonging to every hill and tree and stream.

These beings were their gods. They told wonderful tales about them. They thought that the gods were everywhere and did everything. They believed some god caused every flash of lightning, every springtime crop, every autumn harvest, and every sunset glow.

Of course we now know the real reasons for lightning and seasons and sunsets. But we still like to hear the stories the ancient Greeks told about their gods. We call these stories myths. Even though we know the myths aren't true, we enjoy them because they are such wonderful stories.

The ancient Greeks believed that many of their greatest gods and goddesses lived on a mountain that rose high into the clouds, called Mount Olympus. From the high peaks of Mount Olympus, the gods looked down at the world below. They helped the people they liked and hurt the people they did not like.

The Greeks believed the gods had magical powers. They could change into animals, fly through the air, or hurl thunderbolts from the sky.

Still, in the myths, these gods often act very much like people. They argue, they play tricks, they fall in love.

2

Zeus was the greatest of all the gods and the king of them all. The Greeks usually pictured him as a large, strong man with long hair and a flowing beard. If he was angry, he thundered and hurled shafts of lightning to the earth.

Hera was Zeus's wife. She was a tall, beautiful goddess with yellow hair and blazing eyes. She could be charming at times, and at other times very bitter and jealous. She was almost the only one who was not afraid of Zeus.

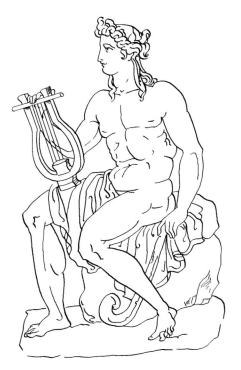

Then there was Phoebus Apollo, the god of the sun and of music. He played upon the lyre and sang the most beautiful songs, so that even the gods were charmed.

Athena was the goddess of wisdom, a very noble goddess, strong yet gentle. She gave to men the best of all gifts, wisdom.

Hephaestus, the god of fire, was the worker among the gods. He built the palaces in which the gods lived. He made the armor they wore, the chariots they drove, and the tables from which they ate at their banquets. If the gods wanted anything made, from a palace to a pair of golden shoes, they went down to Hephaestus, where he worked in his shop underneath Mount Etna.

It is said that Hephaestus once displeased his father Zeus, so that Zeus threw him from Mount Olympus. He was a whole day in falling, and was so injured by his fall that he was always lame afterwards. Still, he was very wise, and the gods liked him for the beautiful things he made for them.

As Phoebus Apollo was god of the sun, Artemis was the goddess of the moon. These two were brother and sister. They furnished nearly all the light men had by day or night. Artemis was tall and strong and swift, and as good a hunter as her brother. In fact, she was also the goddess of hunting.

Ares was the cruel god of war. He rejoiced in the noise and blood of battle. Wherever he went, destruction followed.

Aphrodite was the goddess of love and beauty. She was the most beautiful of all the goddesses, and King Zeus's favorite daughter. No one could look upon her without loving her.

Aphrodite had a son, Eros, a rascal who had a bow and arrow that he used to torment both gods and men. Whoever was struck by one of his arrows was sure to fall in love with the first person he afterwards met. As Eros was not at all careful whom he wounded, or when or where, he caused a great deal of trouble.

Hermes, another son of Zeus, was Zeus's messenger. He wore wings on his hat and on his sandals. Whenever Zeus wished to send news to the earth, Hermes would fly down faster than you can think. He invented the lyre upon which Phoebus Apollo played, and gave it to him for a present.

These gods, and sometimes others, used to meet in the banquet hall of Zeus and talk over their own affairs and the affairs of men. The food they ate was called ambrosia, and the drink, nectar—food and drink for the gods alone.

These banquets were not always pleasant, for the gods did not always agree. Sometimes they had very bitter and very foolish quarrels, as when three of the goddesses quarreled over which of them was the fairest.

Zeus had two brothers who did not live on Mount Olympus, though they were great gods. Their names were Poseidon and Hades.

Poseidon was the ruler of the sea. He could make the oceans calm and quiet, or stir up giant, crashing waves.

Hades ruled the underworld, the dark regions underneath the earth where, the Greeks believed, people went when they died.

About the Names of Greek and Roman Gods

After the Greeks, another great people rose to power. These people, the Romans, lived in the land we now call Italy. The Romans borrowed many ideas and customs from the Greeks, including their religion. The Romans worshipped the same gods as the Greeks, but called them by different names, as shown in the following table. When you read myths in this and other books, you will sometimes see the Greek names, and sometimes the Roman.

Greek name	Roman name	
Zeus	Jupiter	king of the gods
Hera	Juno	wife of Zeus, queen of the gods
Athena	Minerva	goddess of wisdom
Aphrodite	Venus	goddess of love and beauty
Eros	Cupid	god of love, son of Aphrodite
Ares	Mars	god of war
Artemis	Diana	goddess of the moon and hunting
Demeter	Ceres	goddess of corn and growing things
Hephaestus	Vulcan	god of fire and the forge
Hermes	Mercury	the messenger god
Persephone	Proserpina	daughter of Demeter
Phoebus	Apollo	god of the sun, music, and poetry
Poseidon	Neptune	god of the sea
Hades	Pluto	god of the underworld

THE NAMING OF A GREAT CITY

Long ago the people of a far country built a beautiful city. It stood on a high hill overlooking the blue sea. The people laid out the streets with care and crowned the hill with beautiful buildings. The city was very fair to look upon.

"What shall we call our beautiful city?" said the people.

"Name it for me," said Poseidon, the great god of the sea. "I will make your city stronger than any other city on the earth."

"Nay, call it for me," said Athena, the goddess of wisdom. "The gifts that I can give you are worth far more than any gift of strength."

The people of the city did not know how to choose between Poseidon and Athena. "We are only people of the Earth," they said. "How can we decide between the gods?"

So they called to Zeus, the king of the gods: "Great Zeus, tell us what to do. For whom shall we name our beautiful city on the hill?"

Zeus answered, "Both Athena and Poseidon offer you good gifts. Let them bring you their gifts. The one who brings the better gift may claim the city. I myself will be the judge."

When the day of the contest came, all the people of the city gathered together. Zeus then told the god of the sea to bring forth his gift.

Poseidon appeared, leading by the bridle a shining war-horse, strong, swift, and harnessed for battle.

"I offer you war, glory, and power," he said, and the people of the city cheered loud and long.

Now it was Athena's turn. She came forward quietly, carrying something in her hand. Kneeling down before the people, she dug a hole in the ground and placed in it a tiny seed.

A leaf appeared, then a stalk, and then a tree, covered with glossy green leaves and laden with fruit. It was an olive tree.

Athena turned and faced the people. "In this tree is life, peace, and plenty," she said.

The people stood in silence waiting for the great judge to speak.

Then said Zeus, "Athena brings the better gift. The city shall be called Athens."

With one voice, the people took up the cry, "Athens! Athens! The city shall be named for Athena. She has given us the greater gift!"

THE STORY OF ARACHNE

In the city of Athens in the days of long ago, there lived a maiden named Arachne.

Arachne was skilled in the art of spinning and weaving. Not one of the maidens of Athens could spin such fine thread or weave such wonderful cloth as she could.

As time went on, Arachne grew vain and proud. "I am the most wonderful spinner in the world," she said.

"Next to our great goddess Athena," added the good people of Athens.

"Nay," said Arachne boldly, "I do not fear even Athena's skill and power. I know that I can spin as well as she."

"Take care," said the wise people of Athens. "Take care, for your boasting may anger Athena."

Still Arachne did not heed their warning. She grew more vain and boasted more and more. At last the goddess took notice of her foolish boasting.

One day as Arachne was working at her web, an old woman appeared before her.

"My dear," said the stranger, "you boast that you are as skillful as Athena. Try your skill with the maidens, but do not strive with the goddess."

"I am not afraid of Athena," said the maiden. "Let her try her skill with me if she dare."

Then the stranger threw back her dark cloak and showed herself—the beautiful, golden-haired, gray-eyed Athena. "I am ready," she said.

The other maidens were frightened. Only Arachne was not afraid. "Let us begin," she said.

"First, hear this," said Athena. "If your cloth is best, I will weave no more. But if mine is best, you will never weave again. Do you agree?"

"I agree," said Arachne.

Then the people of Athens looked on in wonder as the goddess and the maiden worked at their looms.

Athena wove into her cloth pictures of the great gods—Zeus and Hera, Apollo and Poseidon, and all the others. No one had ever seen anything so wonderful as her pictures.

Arachne had great skill, but the pictures that she wove were not noble and beautiful like Athena's. They showed her own proud spirit.

As soon as her cloth was finished, Arachne looked at the other cloth. She knew that it was much more beautiful than hers. She was filled with grief and anger. "If I can never weave again, how can I live? All my joy in life is gone. Let me die."

"Nay," said Athena, "you shall not die. You shall go on spinning and weaving forever." And with a touch, she turned Arachne into the first spider, which ran to a corner and quickly wove a beautiful, shining web.

"You and your kind," said Athena, "shall always be the greatest spinners and weavers on the earth."

THE STORY OF PROSERPINA

1

An old myth tells us of a king whose name was Pluto, and whose home was deep down in the earth where the rays of the sun never shine.

In all the realms of this king there was no joy of life, no light of day. His was a world of grief, tears, and the shades of night. And so at times he came up to the land of love and hope and joy to find, if he could, something that would cheer his sad life and make it less full of woe.

One day, when the fields were bright with blooms, King Pluto thought that he would ride out and see some of the fair things that had been born of the earth and sun. To see these things, he hoped, might touch a spring of joy in his sad heart.

He rode up by way of Mount Etna, and out through the clouds of steam that pour from its top. Then, with a sharp word to his steeds, he drove in great haste down the steep slopes and did not stop till he reached the green fields at their base.

2

Some girls who lived in that place had gone out to spend the day in the fields. With them was a fair young maid whose name was Proserpina, the child of Ceres. The sun was warm, the sky was fair, the grass was soft. The girls ran here and there, as free as the wild birds of the wood, and had no thought of fear or harm.

At last Proserpina, tired of play, sat down on a stone to rest. The girls that were with her ran on and were soon out of sight. Then, all at once, she heard a strange sound as of wheels and the tramp of hoofs. Before she could run home to the safe arms of Ceres, a black chariot drawn by four coal-black steeds was at her side.

In the chariot stood a tall, sad-faced man, dark-eyed and pale, who wore a crown of gold on his head. Proserpina screamed and stood still—it was all that she could do. Then she was caught up in the strong arms of King Pluto, who at the same time swung his long whip in the air and cried out to his steeds, "On, on, ye dark ones! Race with the stars that shoot through the sky! Speed ye! Speed ye!"

Poor Proserpina screamed and tried to leap from the chariot, but the stern, sad king soothed her fears with kind words, and told her that so long as she would stay with him, she should be free from harm. Then a sheet of flame shot up and shut out the light of day. The steeds, the chariot, the king, and the maid went down, down, down, and were seen no more.

3

When news was brought to good Ceres that her child was lost, she did not faint or cry out in her great grief, for she was too brave and wise to do that. But she went out at once in search of her child, and she vowed that she would find her or come back no more.

With a black veil wound round her head, and with a torch in her hand, she crossed the seas and went from land to land, and asked all that dwelt on the earth if they had seen her child. For a whole year she searched in vain. Then she thought that she would ask Helios, who drives the chariot of the sun through the skies.

"Great Helios," she said, "I know that your eye takes in the whole world, and that all the deeds of men are known to you. Tell me, I pray you, have you seen my lost child, Proserpina?"

Kind Helios was glad that she had come to him. Yes, he had seen Proserpina. He had seen Pluto as he rushed down from Etna. He had seen him lift the child from the ground into his black car. He had seen the wild leap down Mount Etna's throat.

"The maid is in Pluto's dark realms," he said, "and Pluto has made her his queen. But he would not have seized her as he did without permission from Jupiter, the king of earth and air."

Then Ceres gave way to grief and rage. She sent word to Jupiter that no fruits or grain should grow in all the world while Pluto kept Proserpina in his dark home. For it was Ceres, men said, who gave life to the trees and plants and made them bloom and bear fruit.

4

Jupiter and the great ones that were with him knew that Ceres would be true to her word, and the thought filled them with fear. If there should be no fruit or grains for men, and no food for them but fish and flesh, they would soon be as wild as in the old, old times, and there would be no good deeds done in all the world.

"The best thing that we can do," said Jupiter, "is to bring Proserpina back."

So he ordered Mercury, who had winged feet, to go down to the halls of Pluto and fetch the lost maid back.

Pluto was glad to see Mercury, but he frowned when he learned why he had come.

"Do you know the law?" he asked.

"What law?" said Mercury.

"There is a law that no one can break," said Pluto. "I will read it to you."

Then he took a black book from a shelf on the wall, and read these words: "That one, be it god or man, maid or child, who tastes food while in the land of Pluto, shall not go thence so long as the world stands."

Then Mercury asked Proserpina if food had passed her lips since the day that she had come to Pluto's land. She told him that she had been too sad to think of food. Yet once she had plucked some bright red fruit that grew on a tree by the banks of the dark stream that men call the Styx.

"Did you taste it?"

"Yes, I took one small bite, and then threw the rest far from me."

King Pluto laughed loud and long. But Mercury asked him, "What kind of bright red fruit grows on the banks of the dark stream that you call the Styx?"

"Pomegranates," said the king.

"Is a pomegranate food?" asked Mercury. "At the best not more than one third of it is fit to eat. The rest is skin and seeds."

Then he took Proserpina back to the bright earth. Ceres stood at the door of the great cave, and Mercury placed her dear child in her arms. Then he told her that, for two-thirds of each year, Proserpina might stay with her and make her and all the world glad. But he said that, for the rest of the time, she must go back to Pluto's dark realms.

And so it is that, when Proserpina stays in the
dark lands of Pluto, the days grow chill with frost and
snow, and the grains of corn lie dead in the ground.
But when the sad-faced king brings her back, then the
days grow bright and warm. Then Ceres is happy, and
the stalks begin to grow and the buds of the fruit trees
burst forth.

A Flight Through the Sky

Long ago on a faraway island there lived a man named Daedalus.

Daedalus was famed throughout the land for his skill with his hands. No other man of his time was so clever in building. His mind was always full of plans to make something new.

But though he was held in great honor, Daedalus was really a prisoner. The cruel king of the island knew how skillful he was and would not let him go away.

As time went on, Daedalus grew weary of his life on the island and wished to escape. But it was impossible for him to get away by sea. On every side the king's strong ships kept watch.

For a long time Daedalus wondered how he could escape. At last he hit upon a daring plan.

"The king may control the land and sea," he said, "but he does not control the air. I will go that way."

No man had ever before tried to do what he planned to do. He planned to make two sets of wings, one for himself and one for his young son Icarus, so that they could fly away.

He set to work secretly collecting feathers, small ones and large ones. Then he made a light frame of wood, with cloth stretched over it. Very carefully he laid the feathers all over the frame, and held them firmly in place with wax.

Night after night he worked in secret, until at last he had finished a pair of wings. As soon as these were ready, he strapped them on his son's shoulders. He showed the boy how to flap them like a bird, and slowly young Icarus learned to fly.

Each night Daedalus secretly worked on the second pair of wings, and each night Icarus tried his skill at flying.

At last all was ready. Early in the morning, Daedalus and his son stole down to the beach, carrying their wings.

As the father strapped the boy's wings in place, he said, "Icarus, my son, listen to what I say. Be sure to keep the middle track. If you fly too low over the sea, your wings will get wet. If you go too high, the heat of the sun will melt the wax on your wings. Be very careful. Do not fly too close to the sun."

Icarus promised, eager to be off. Then as Daedalus gave the word, they raised their wings and rose up, up over the sea like great birds.

The morning sun shone on their feathers so that they glistened like gold. The cool air from the ocean touched their faces. A great thrill went through the boy as he felt himself soaring up through the morning air.

He forgot his father's warning. He swooped down to the waves, and then rose again higher and higher into the sky.

Suddenly, before he could stop himself, he had flown too near the hot sun. The burning heat melted the wax. The feathers loosened and fell in a soft shower into the water.

In vain Icarus flapped his arms. His wings were now useless. Down he dropped—down, down to the sea.

"Icarus," cried his father. "Icarus, where are you?" No answer came. Only the feathers floating on the water showed him what had happened.

Poor Daedalus flew on till he came safely to land. But he was so sad at the loss of his son that he never used his wings again.

POETRY

THE WORLD IS
SO FULL

HAPPY THOUGHT

The world is so full of a number of things,
I'm sure we should all be as happy as kings.

– Robert Louis Stevenson

WHAT IS ONCE LOVED

What is once loved
You will find
Is always yours
From that day.
Take it home
In your mind
And nothing ever
Can take it away.

– Elizabeth Coatsworth

PIPPA'S SONG

The year's at the spring,
And day's at the morn;
Morning's at seven;
The hillside's dew-pearled;
The lark's on the wing;
The snail's on the thorn:
God's in his heaven—
All's right with the world!

– Robert Browning

THE CHILD'S WORLD

Great, wide, beautiful, wonderful World,
With the wonderful water round you curled,
And the wonderful grass upon your breast,—
World, you are beautifully dressed.

The wonderful air is over me,
And the wonderful wind is shaking the tree,
It walks on the water, and whirls the mills,
And talks to itself on the tops of the hills.

You, friendly Earth! how far do you go,
With the wheat-fields that nod and the rivers that flow,
With cities and gardens, and cliffs, and isles,
And people upon you for thousands of miles?

Ah, you are so great, and I am so small,
I tremble to think of you, World, at all;
And yet, when I said my prayers today,
A whisper inside me seemed to say,
"You are more than the Earth, though you are such a dot:
You can love and think, and the Earth can not!"

– W. B. Rands

SUPPOSE

Suppose, my little lady,
Your doll should break her head;
Could you make it whole by crying
Till your eyes and nose were red?
And wouldn't it be pleasanter
To treat it as a joke,
And say you're glad 'twas Dolly's,
And not your head, that broke?

Suppose you're dressed for walking,
And rain comes pouring down;
Will it clear off any sooner
Because you scold and frown?
And wouldn't it be nicer
For you to smile than pout,
And so make sunshine in the house
When there is none without?

Suppose your task, my little man,
Is very hard to get;
Will it make it any easier
For you to sit and fret?
And wouldn't it be wiser,
Than waiting like a dunce,
To go to work in earnest
And learn a thing at once?

Suppose that some boys have a horse,
And some a coach and pair;
Will it tire you less while walking
To say, "It isn't fair"?
And wouldn't it be nobler
To keep your temper sweet,
And in your heart be thankful
You can walk upon your feet?

– Phoebe Cary

LITTLE WORDS OF KINDNESS

A little word in kindness spoken,
A motion or a tear,
Has often healed the heart that's broken,
And made a friend sincere.

A word, a look, has crushed to earth
Full many a budding flower,
Which, had a smile but owned its birth,
Would bless life's darkest hour.

Then think it not an idle thing
A pleasant word to speak:
The face you wear, the thoughts you bring,
A heart may heal or break.

— *Anonymous*

POETRY

ANIMAL FRIENDS

THE HAIRY DOG

My dog's so furry I've not seen
His face for years and years:
His eyes are buried out of sight,
I only guess his ears.

When people ask me for his breed,
I do not know or care:
He has the beauty of them all
Hidden beneath his hair.

– Herbert Asquith

I'VE GOT A DOG

I've got a dog as thin as a rail,
He's got fleas all over his tail.
Every time his tail goes flop,
The fleas on the bottom all hop to the top.

– Anonymous

A KITTEN

He's nothing much but fur
And two round eyes of blue,
He has a giant purr
And a midget mew.

He darts and pats the air,
He starts and cocks his ear,
When there is nothing there
For him to see and hear.

He runs around in rings,
But why we cannot tell;
With sideways leaps he springs
At things invisible—

Then half-way through a leap
His startled eyeballs close,
And he drops off to sleep
With one paw on his nose.

– Eleanor Farjeon

CAT

My cat
Is quiet.
She moves without a sound.
Sometimes she stretches herself curving
On tiptoe.
Sometimes she crouches low
And creeping.

Sometimes she rubs herself against a chair,
And there
With a *miew* and a *miew*
And a purrrr   purrrr   purrrr
She curls up
And goes to sleep.

My cat
Lives through a black hole
Under the house.
So one day I
Crawled in after her.

And it was dark
And I sat
And didn't know
Where to go.
And then—

Two yellow-white
Round little lights
Came moving . . . moving . . . toward me.
And there
With a *miew* and a *miew*
And a purrrr   purrrr   purrrr
My cat
Rubbed, soft, against me.

And I knew
The lights
Were MY CAT'S EYES
In the dark.

– *Dorothy Baruch*

BLISS

Let me fetch sticks,
Let me fetch stones,
Throw me your bones,
Teach me your tricks.

When you go ride,
Let me go run,
You in the sun,
Me at your side;

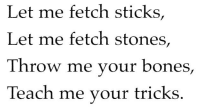

When you go swim,
Let me go too
Both lost in blue
Up to the brim;

Let me do this,
Let me do that—
What you are at,
That is my bliss.

— *Eleanor Farjeon*

116

THE ELEPHANT

The elephant is very large
And clumsy as a wooden barge,
With legs like tree-trunks, yet he's mild
And gentle as a little child.

The elephant walks far away
And sees strange children in their play,
And carries logs and iron bars
As easily as motor-cars.

The elephant's a great big beast—
Not beautiful, but good, at least,
Strong as a tree, but withal mild
And gentle as a little child.

– Annette Wynne

THE SILENT SNAKE

The birds go fluttering in the air,
The rabbits run and skip,
Brown squirrels race along the bough,
The mayflies rise and dip;
But while these creatures play and leap,
The silent snake goes creepy-creep!

The birds, they sing and whistle loud,
The busy insects hum,
The squirrels chat, the frogs say "Croak!"
But the snake is always dumb.
With not a sound through grasses deep,
The silent snake goes creepy-creep!

– Anonymous

POETRY

NATURE'S WAY

APRIL RAIN SONG

Let the rain kiss you.
Let the rain beat upon your head with silver liquid drops.
Let the rain sing you a lullaby.

The rain makes still pools on the sidewalk.
The rain makes running pools in the gutter.
The rain plays a little sleep-song on our roof at night—

And I love the rain.

– Langston Hughes

THE RAINDROP'S RIDE

Some little drops of water
Whose home was in the sea,
To go upon a journey
Once happened to agree.

A white cloud was their carriage;
Their horse, a playful breeze;
And over town and country
They rode along at ease.

But oh! there were so many,
At last the carriage broke,
And to the ground came tumbling
Those frightened little folk.

Among the grass and flowers
They then were forced to roam,
Until a brooklet found them
And carried them all home.

– Anonymous

THE BUILDING OF THE NEST

They'll come again to the apple tree—
    Robin and all the rest—
When the orchard branches are fair to see,
    In the snow of the blossom dressed;
And the prettiest thing in the world will be
    The building of the nest.

Weaving it well, so round and trim,
    Hollowing it with care,
Nothing too far away for him,
    Nothing for her too fair,
Hanging it safe on the topmost limb,
    Their castle in the air.

Ah! mother bird, you'll have weary days
    When the eggs are under your breast,
And shadow may darken the dancing rays
    When the wee ones leave the nest;
But they'll find their wings in a glad amaze,
    And God will see to the rest.

So come to the trees with all your train
　　When the apple blossoms blow;
Through the April shimmer of sun and rain,
　　Go flying to and fro;
And sing to our hearts as we watch again
　　Your fairy building grow.

– Margaret E. Sangster

Winter Jewels

A million little diamonds
    Twinkled on the trees,
And all the little maidens said,
    "A jewel, if you please!"
But while they held their hands outstretched,
    To catch the diamonds gay,
A million little sunbeams came
    And stole them all away.

— Mary F. Butts

PUSSY WILLOWS

I came on them yesterday (merely by chance),
Those newly born pussies, asleep on a branch;
Each curled up so tight in a fluff of a ball
That I could not see ear-points or tail-tips at all;
But I thought that I heard, when the March wind was stirring,
A soft little sound like the note of purring.
I wonder if they would have leaped from their bough
And arched their wee backs with a frightened "Meow!"
If I dared to tell them in one warning cry
That a fierce patch of dogwood was growing close by.

– Rowena Bastin Bennett

THE SECRET

We have a secret, just we three,
The robin, and I, and the sweet cherry tree;
The bird told the tree, and the tree told me,
And nobody knows it but just we three.

But of course the robin knows it best,
Because she built the—I shan't tell the rest;
And laid the four little—something in it—
I'm afraid I shall tell it every minute.

But if the tree and the robin don't peep,
I'll try my best the secret to keep;
Though I know when the little birds fly about
Then the whole secret will be out.

– Anonymous

TEXT CREDITS AND SOURCES

Poems:

"April Rain Song" from *The Collected Poems of Langston Hughes* by Langston Hughes, © 1994 by The Estate of Langston Hughes. Used by permission of Alfred A. Knopf, a division of Random House, Inc., and Harold Ober Associates, Inc.

"Bliss" and "A Kitten" from *Blackbird Has Spoken* by Eleanor Farjeon, published by Macmillan, London © 1933 by Eleanor Farjeon. Reprinted by permission of David Higham Associates.

Stories:

"Chipmunk and Bear" reprinted with permission from *Iroquois Stories* © 1985 by Joseph Bruchac. Published by The Crossing Press, Freedom, California.

Other stories adapted from:

Charlie and His Kitten Topsy, by Helen Hill and Violet Maxwell (New York: Macmillan, 1922)

Everyday Classics, Third Reader, Franklin T. Baker, Ashley H. Thorndike, and Mildred Batchelder (New York: Macmillan, 1922)

The Merrill Readers: Third Reader, Franklin B. Dyer and Mary J. Brady (New York: Charles E. Merrill Company, 1915)

Stepping Stones to Literature, A Fourth Reader, Sarah Louise Arnold and Charles B. Gilbert (New York: Silver Burdett and Company, 1897)

Story Hour Readers Revised, Book Three, Ida Coe and Alice C. Dillion, (New York: American Book Company, 1914)

While every care has been taken to trace and acknowledge copyright, the editors tender their apologies for any accidental infringement when copyright has proven untraceable. They would be pleased to include the appropriate acknowledgement in any subsequent edition of this publication.

Editor: John Holdren

Art Director: Steve Godwin

Designer: Jayoung Cho

Illustrators:
Dan Boris
Jayoung Cho
Vince McGinley

ISBN: 1-931728-34-8